William H. Johnson

COLORING BOOK

Born in South Carolina to a poor African American family, William H. Johnson (1901–1970) moved to New York at age seventeen. He worked a variety of jobs to pay for an art education at the prestigious National Academy of Design, where he earned numerous awards and the respect of his teachers and fellow students.

Johnson spent the late 1920s in France, absorbing the lessons of modernism. As a result, his work became more expressive and emotional. During this same period, he met and fell in love with Danish artist Holcha Krake. The couple married and spent most of the 1930s in Scandinavia, where he painted portraits of fisherman, landscapes, and the spectacular mountains and fjords in the land of the midnight sun. By the late '30s, the threat of war and Johnson's need to "paint his own people" had convinced him to return to New York, where he created powerful scenes of African American life.

Johnson's later life was plagued by illness, and he spent his final years in a Long Island hospital. After his death, his entire life's work was almost disposed of to save storage fees but was rescued by friends at the last moment. Over a thousand artworks by Johnson are now part of the collection of the Smithsonian American Art Museum.

Smithsonian American Art Museum

Pomegranate **kids**®

AGES 3 to 103!

All the original artworks are by William H. Johnson (American, 1901–1970).
Collection credit: Smithsonian American Art Museum, Gift of the Harmon Foundation.

1. *Sweet Adeline*, about 1940, tempera and pen and ink on paper mounted on paperboard

2. *Sowing*, about 1940, oil on burlap

3. *Flowers*, about 1944–45, oil on paperboard

4. *Breakdown*, about 1940–41, tempera, pen and ink, and pencil on paper

5. *Chalet in the Mountains*, about 1938, oil on burlap

6. *Lift Up Thy Voice and Sing*, about 1942–44, oil on paperboard

7. *Ferry Boat Trip*, about 1943–44, oil on paperboard

8. *Jitterbugs (I)*, about 1940–41, gouache and pen and ink on paperboard

9. *Street Life, Harlem*, about 1939–40, oil on plywood

10. *Art Class*, about 1939–40, oil on plywood

11. *Blind Musician*, about 1940, oil on plywood

12. *Li'L Sis*, 1944, oil on paperboard

13. *Going to Church*, about 1940–41, screenprint on paper

14. *Wedding Couple*, about 1940, oil on plywood

15. *Farewell*, about 1942, tempera, pen and ink, and pencil on paper

16. *Dockyard*, about 1941–43, tempera, pen and ink, and pencil on paper mounted on paperboard

17. *Flower to Teacher*, about 1944, oil on paperboard

18. *Three Little Children*, 1944, oil on paperboard

19. *Deep South*, about 1940–41, screenprint on paper

20. *Folk Family*, about 1944, oil on plywood

21. *Still Life—Flowers*, about 1944–45, oil on paperboard

22. *Children Dance*, about 1944, oil on plywood

Pomegranate Communications, Inc.
19018 NE Portal Way, Portland OR 97230
800 227 1428   www.pomegranate.com
Color illustrations © 2014 Smithsonian Institution
Line drawings © Pomegranate Communications, Inc.
Item No. CB160

Designed by Stephanie Odeh
Line drawings by LeeAnne Gibney

Printed in Korea

23 22 21 20 19 18 17 16 15 14   10 9 8 7 6 5 4 3 2 1

Distributed by Pomegranate Europe Ltd.
Unit 1, Heathcote Business Centre, Hurlbutt Road
Warwick, Warwickshire CV34 6TD, UK
[+44] 0 1926 430111
sales@pomeurope.co.uk

This product is in compliance with the Consumer Product Safety Improvement Act of 2008 (CPSIA) and any subsequent amendments thereto. A General Conformity Certificate concerning Pomegranate's compliance with the CPSIA is available on our website at www.pomegranate.com, or by request at 800 227 1428. For additional CPSIA-required tracking details, contact Pomegranate at 800 227 1428.

1. *Sweet Adeline*

2. Sowing

3. *Flowers*

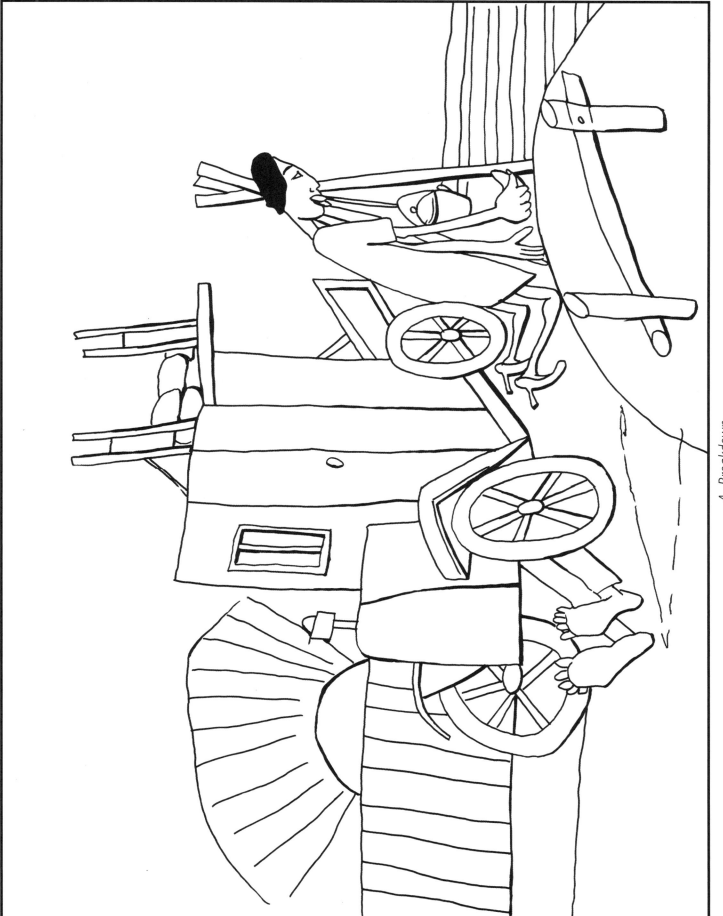

4. Breakdown

5. Chalet in the Mountains

6. Lift Up Thy Voice and Sing

7. Ferry Boat Trip

8. *Jitterbugs (I)*

9. *Street Life, Harlem*

10. *Art Class*

11. Blind Musician

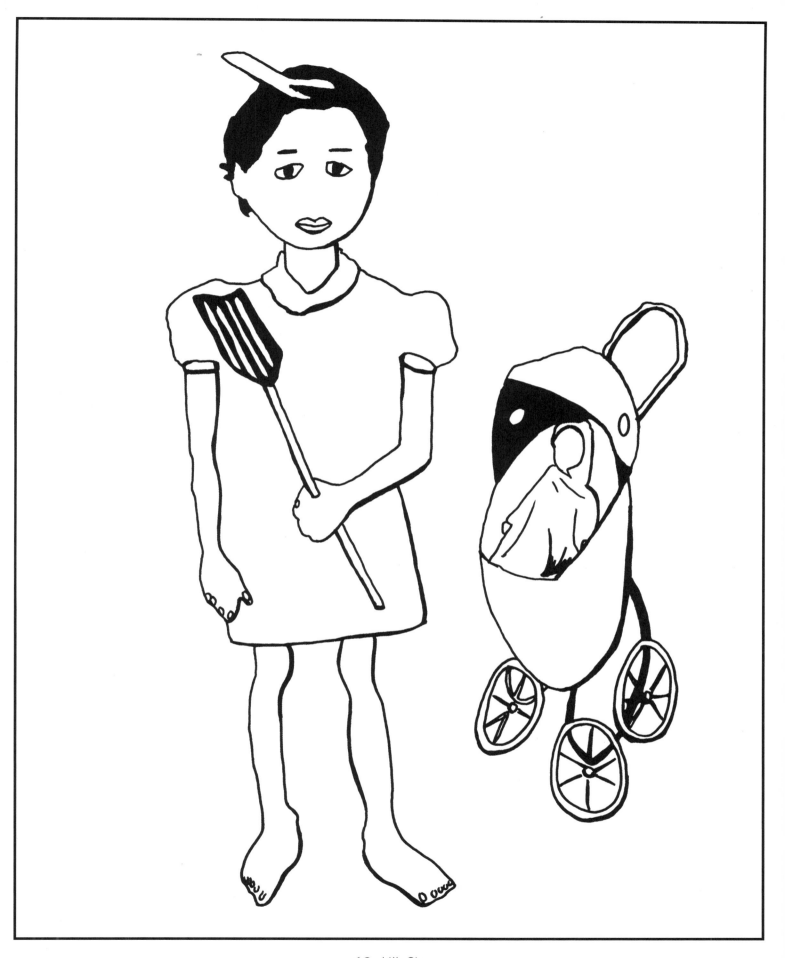

12. Li'L Sis

13. Going to Church

14. *Wedding Couple*

15. Farewell

16. Dockyard

17. Flower to Teacher

18. *Three Little Children*

19. *Deep South*

20. *Folk Family*

21. *Still Life—Flowers*

22. Children Dance

Draw and color your own picture here!